CN00968056

To Gethin, our seaside baby.

First Impression—2002

ISBN 1 84323 106 9 (regular)
ISBN 1 84323 155 7 (big book)

© text: Ruth Morgan
© illustrations: Suzanne Carpenter

Ruth Morgan and Suzanne Carpenter
have asserted their rights under the
Copyright, Designs and Patents Act,
1988, to be identified as Author and
Illustrator of this Work.

This title is published with the support of
the Arts Council of Wales.

Cover Design: Olwen Fowler

Printed in Wales at
Gomer Press, Llandysul, Ceredigion SA44 4QL.

Jumping the Waves

Sglod's favourite poems

RUTH MORGAN

Illustrated by
SUZANNE CARPENTER

PONT

Contents

Snorkledog

Snorkle-orkle-orkling
Underneath the pier
In my mask and flappy flippers
Frightening creatures far and near.

They all race to hide
As I gurgle up beside them
Like a one-eyed burbling monster
Filling fishies full of fear!

The only trouble is . . .

Twinkle twinkle little starfish,
How I wonder what you are, fish.
I would keep you as a pet
But you might make the carpet wet.

Crinkle crinkle little crab,
How your pincers love to jab.
I could keep you in my sink
But it might make the bathroom stink.

Tunnelling

Tunnelling,
Burrowing deep
Like sand moles.

Scooping,
Scraping away,
Patting wet walls.

Collapse!
Digging, faster,
Saving it, just.

Secret
Underground passages,
Caverns in darkness.

Sand King

The Sand King on the beach
With his slanty mouth of stones
And his seagull feather crown
Stares in anger at the sea.

"Get back!" he shouts again
But the waves don't hear his moans.
They creep closer up the beach
And try to nibble at his toes.

One by one, his twenty towers
Start to crumble-tumble down
As the foaming, fizzing water
Sucks and tears the sandy walls.

Now the Sand King watches sadly
As one great moat surrounds him,
All his castles gone, their bright flags
Washing up and down around him

And the tide, still coming in
Pulls his seaweed cloak away.
He's returning to the beach,
The king who couldn't rule the waves.

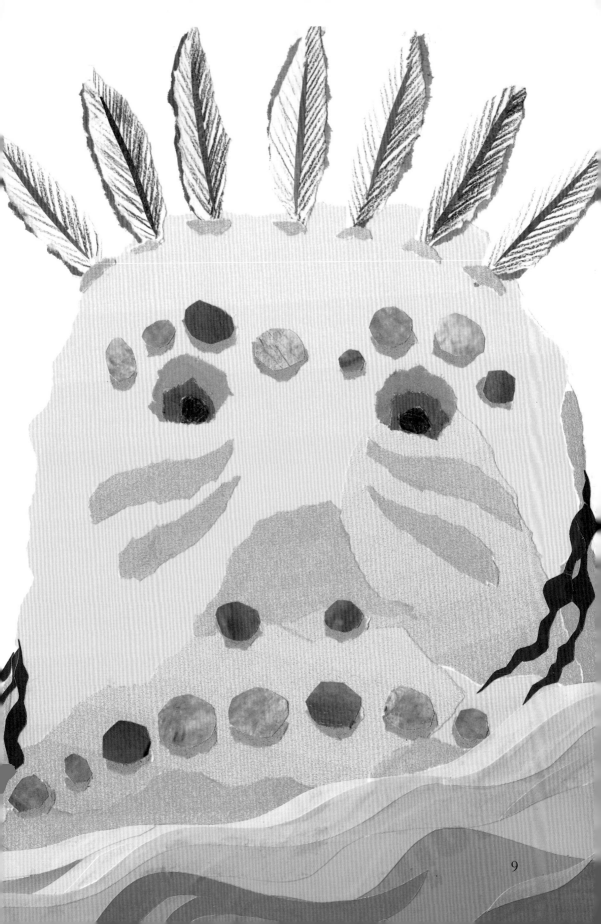

9

Shell

Listen closely to my shell oh what secrets it may tell . . .

Listen closely to my shell oh what secrets it may tell . . .

Listen closely to my shell oh what secrets it may tell . . .

Wave

The edge of the wave lapping

between my toes

Holiday snaps

When you sat on top of the litter bin
Ice cream dribbling down your chin
And you gave the most enormous grin
Hold it...say cheese...

SNAP!

When your bathers fell off in the pool
You didn't notice and tried to look cool
Then turned to wave at your friends from school
Hold it...say cheese...

SNAP!

When the cross old crab caught hold of your toe
You shook and you shook but it wouldn't let go,
When you laughed at the Punch and Judy show
Hold it...say cheese...

SNAP!

Chips

Lick your fingers,
Lick your lips,
Time for lishy, lushy chips
Fizzling fresh from Nellie's fryer,
Enough to set your mouth on fire!
Two big scoops for you and me –
Make mine extra vinegary.
Salty, steamy, golden brown,
Blow a bit to cool them down, then –
Lick your fingers,
Lick your lips,
Time for lishy, lushy chips!

Nellie's Bloomers

What's the time?
Five to nine –
Nellie's bloomers on the line.

Waving, waving in the breeze
Legs that reach below your knees.

Purple, pink and navy blue,
Flowery, spotty, stripy too.

What's the time?
Five to nine –
Nellie's bloomers on the line.

Gift Shop Goodies

The gift shop window is crammed full of goodies,
There's too much to look at,
There's too much to choose:
Cuddly sharks and kaleidoscope keyrings
Lobster binoculars, seasnake tattoos.
Chocolate whales and inflatable flip flops,
A necklace of shells that spell out your name,
A fridge magnet mermaid that sings 'Penblwydd Hapus'
Not once or twice but again and again…
Mindbending tricks that amaze and confuse!
Too much to look at,
Too much to choose.

An octopus teapot for very large families
Pouring out eight cups of tea at a time,
Submarine biscuits and liquorice aliens,
Fizzy fish flavoured with lemon and lime.
Award-winning Welsh cakes you saw on the news!
Too much to look at,
Too much to choose.

Whistling yo-yos that light up like fireflies,
Glittery purses that close up like clams,
Snow-shaker scenes of your favourite castles,
Blue china buckets of novelty jams.
Jigsaws of Abertwt's fabulous views!
Too much to look at,
Too much to choose.

There's too much to look at,
There's too much to choose.

Dolphin Dreaming

Happy dolphin
Leaping with delight
All bright flash and sparkle
Riding the waves
Take me with you
Out to sea one day.

Tiger in the Storm

The storm hunches on low front paws
Muscles quivering,
Preparing to spring,
Its pale eyes watch and wait.
Rain stripes pelt the ground.
A soft rumble starts in its throat
Then works its way down to the echoing belly.
Quick – see its teeth flash,
Hear its tail crack the sky apart,
Better run for your life!
The storm is a ravenous tiger.

Captain Caradog's Sea Shanty

I've sailed around the coast of Wales
Through stormy seas and howling gales,
I've struggled in my little boat
To keep alive and stay afloat…

Now I want to sleep
I just want to sleep
Dozing in my deckchair
I'm dreaming of the deep.

I've battled with an octopus
That weighed as much as a Cardiff bus,
My boat was battered by a shark
When I went fishing after dark…..

Now I want to sleep
I just want to sleep
Down behind the lobster pots
I'm dreaming of the deep.

Pirates chased me round the bay –
It happened just the other day;
I dodged their bullets when they fired
It's no wonder I'm so tired…

Now I want to sleep
Please just let me sleep
Snoring in my hammock
I'm dreaming of the deep.

Something Sticky

"Leave it alone, it's sticky, Ricky,
It's smelly and gooey and green.
Just put it down like a good boy, please –
No, don't wipe your hands on your trouser knees!
If you do that again, I'm taking you home.
It's sticky so leave it alone."

Water Wings

Fancy having wings
That could fly – or swim
High up in the air
Or deep down in the sea.

Up high –
Swimming through the air,
Diving in and out of clouds,
Paddling in the breeze.

Or down deep –
Flying through the water,
Gliding under the waves,
Flapping against the tide.

Here, on the pier,
Slung between the sea and sky
I wonder what that
Would be like?

Peer through the Pier

peer through

the cracks in the

pier make a wish you

might spy a crab

or a silvery fish

I Didn't See The Dragon . . .

I didn't *see* the dragon
But I heard his mighty roar
As the waves rushed in like hungry teeth
And CHOMPED upon the shore.

I didn't *see* the dragon
But I smelt his FIERY breath
As the smoke blew from the chip shop door
And scared me half to death!

I didn't *see* the dragon
But I SWEAR I touched his tail
It was slippery as bladderwrack
With periwinkle scales.

So have YOU seen the dragon?
I feel sure he just passed by,
If you follow his sandy claw prints
Then perhaps he'll catch your eye.

Blod and the Band

Thump - a - thump - a - thump - a - thump
A - ching - a - ching - a - ching,
Isn't the sound of the band on the pier
Such a glorious thing?
Whoomp - a - whoomp - a - whoomp - a - whoomp
It really makes our day,
If only Blod the seagull would
Just keep out of our way!

Her squawking, squawking, squawking
Makes the leader stamp and shout,
She flew right down the tuba
And had to be blown out.
She balanced on the cymbals –
We thought it such a cheek,
She split the side of the big bass drum
When she bashed it with her beak!

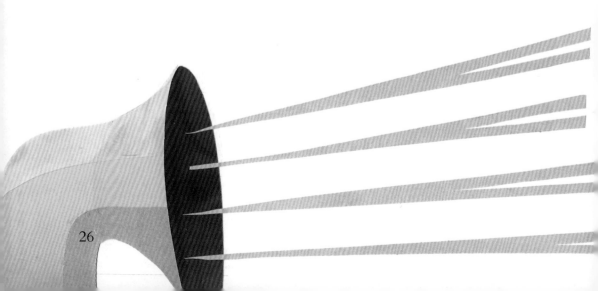

Thump - a - thump - a - thump - a - thump
A - ching - a - ching - a - ching,
Listening to the band is fun
But it's better joining in!

Sandwiches

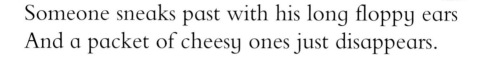

Sandwiches, sandwiches all in a row
Sandwiches, sandwiches, ready to go.

Someone sneaks past with his long floppy ears
And a packet of cheesy ones just disappears.

Sandwiches, sandwiches all in a row
Sandwiches, sandwiches ready to go.

Someone swoops down in the blink of an eye
And a packet of hammy ones head for the sky.

Sandwiches, sandwiches all in a row
Best buy them quickly before they all go!

Lolly

It's m-e-l-t
-i-n-g...Plop! A drip
upon the floor, don't
...Stop! Lick like mad,
once round this side,
once round that.
"What's the matter?"
"It's too hot! My
lolly's crying

r   t
a
s
p   e
p
b   a
e
r   r
r
y   drops."

Lullaby

At the end of the day
Boats bob off to sleep,
Evening stars and streetlights
Reflect across the bay.
Too late for fishing,
White seabirds
Tuck themselves away.